12 PUGNACIOUS PENGUINS

A counting book for kids and adults

Written and illustrated by

Joe Spooner

Edited by Michelle McCann

Publisher's Cataloging in Publication Data

Spooner, Joe
      12 Pugnacious Penguins—a counting book for kids and adults / written and illustrated by Joe
Spooner.—1st ed.
             p. cm.
Summary: Animals from zero to 20 in silly rhyme, with detailed illustrations and interesting facts.
      ISBN: 978-0-9838167-0-5 (Softcover, alk. paper)
[1. Counting—Juvenile fiction. 2. Stories in rhyme.   3. Animals—Fiction] I. Title
PZ7. 513.2/11 2011
[E]—dc22
                Pre-assigned LOC Number: 2011915904

ISBN 978-0-9838168-0-5

ACS, LLC
Portland, Oregon
www.ideasbyacs.com

For my mother, who taught me how to count. And, how to be silly.

And of course, for Patti, John, Norah and Steve.

For their donations and help in getting this book published I would like to thank Oakdale Heights Elementary School, Wade White, Dan and Susan Jordan, Randy Russell and Julie McKim, Karen Hawkins, Pat Spooner, David Streight and Pamela Vohnson, Jeff and Georgiana Rimicci, Chuck and Lois Groshong, Michael and Kate Jakola, Bill and Laurie Gunning, Bill and Lynn Glenn, Jim and Susan Kliewer, Ellen Spooner and Neil Forsgren, Gloria Martinez, John and Gail Butter, Polly Spooner and Terry Hansen, Tom and Erica Swanson, Don Gregonis, Tony and Jemie Miceli, Ross Hawkins and Diane Vines, Greta and Keith Sheppard and Lyle Elementary School.

Just as in *N is for Nostril,* there's a small rodent-like creature hidden in every picture. And some pictures, I guess, have rodents that aren't so hidden. You'll just have to decide which is which.

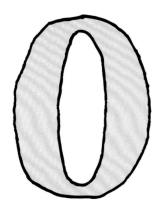

Zero animals on this page.
Zero's where we start.
There's not a lot to look at
When you don't have any art.

One curious coyote
Pawing through a book.
Animals are everywhere,
You ought to take a look.

Because coyotes are so adaptable and clever (you might even say "wily") and because they eat almost anything (anything but tofu—and who can blame them?) their population continues to grow.

In captivity, coyotes can live up to 18 years; in the wild—and this is why it's called the wild—they live only ten to 14 years.

Coyotes have litters of one to 19 pups (yikes!) and after the pups are weaned, both parents feed them regurgitated food. Yep, that means barf. Regurgitated ground squirrel is rumored to be quite tasty.

2

Two hefty, happy hippos
Riding on a bike;
Both are peddling very hard,
Both dressed just alike.

"Hippopotamus" comes from the Greek words for "river horse." The hippo's closest relatives are not elephants and rhinoceroses, but whales and porpoises, which makes for some pretty interesting family get-togethers.

Hippos are born in the water and spend most of their lives there. When they don't order take-out for dinner, hippos eat grass—up to 150 pounds of it a day.

Hippos—so cute and adorable in counting books—have killed more people in Africa than any other animal.

A group of hippos is called a "bloat." Hippos are presently lobbying to have this changed to a "svelte."

3

Three intrepid three-toed
  sloths
On the high trapeze,
Doing deeds of derring-do
While hanging by their
  knees.

Three-toed sloths live up in trees. On
the ground they are slow, v-e-r-y s-l-o-w.
At a full gallop a sloth can go one mile
in six-and-a-half hours. And since sloths
sleep (fortunately, not down by the sea
shore) 20 hours a day, that mile can take
almost two days of c-r-a-w-l-i-n-g.
  The three-toed sloth's prehistoric
ancestors were the "Giant Ground
Sloths," as big as modern-day elephants.
These sloths began migrating to the
northern hemisphere about 3.5 million
years ago. The price of gas was much
cheaper then.

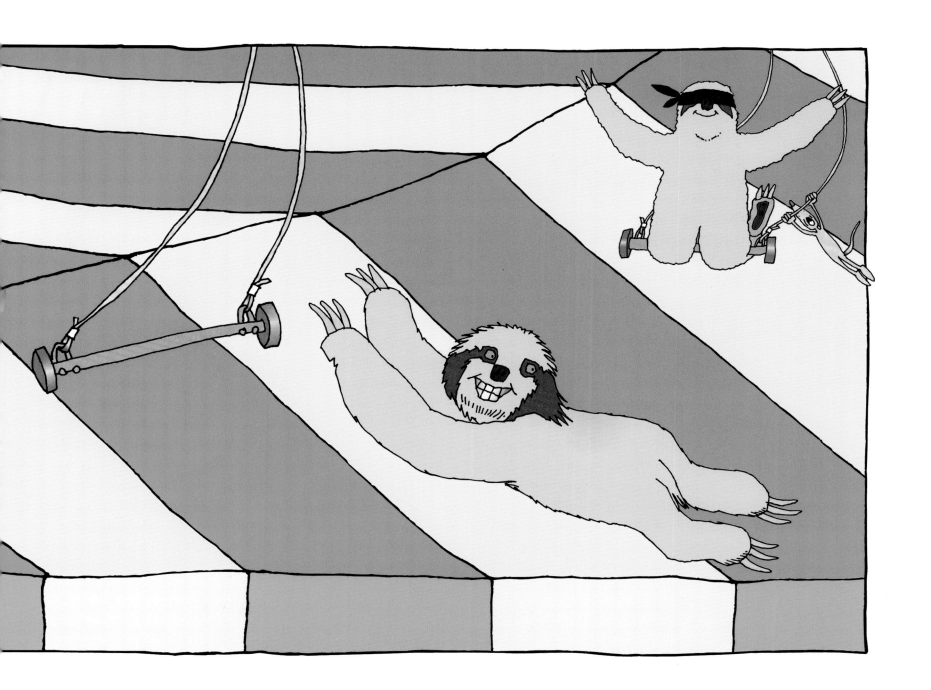

4

Four parading polar bears
On the avenue,
Their fans are cheering
    madly
As they march past
    two-by-two.

Polar bears live in the northern
hemisphere. Why? Because vicious,
bear-eating penguins live in the
southern hemisphere.

Polar bears are huge, weighing
up to 1,500 pounds. They survive
in arctic temperatures as low as
−50°F and have more problems with
overheating than they do with being
too cold.

The polar bear's sense of smell
is very keen. It can smell a seal 20
miles away. If the seal isn't wearing
deodorant, 25 miles away.

Polar bear fur is immaculately
white once each year when they molt,
but slowly yellows from seal blubber
stains—they absolutely refuse to
wear bibs.

5

Five picnicking pink
 flamingos
Head down in the swamp,
Searching for some
 shrimp to eat
Chomp, chomp, chomp,
 chomp, chomp.

Pink flamingos are pink because of what they eat: shrimp. Lots of shrimp. They suck mud and water into the front of their curved beaks and pump it out the sides, using filters to separate shrimp and other small creatures from the mud. You don't want to be around flamingos when they are having a food fight.

Pink flamingos stand about 50 inches tall and weigh up to seven-and-a-half pounds. Plastic flamingos stand as tall or as short as they please and weigh practically nothing.

Six shaggy Shetland ponies
Sleeping in a row,
Dreaming dreams of
   vaudeville
With a chorus line of crows.

Sturdy little Shetland ponies can pull twice their weight.

Because of their small size and their strength, they were brought to England from the Shetland Islands in the 1850s to work in coal mines, where they pulled carts full of workers and coal. Some of these ponies were born in the mines, worked their entire lives there and died without ever coming to the surface.

Today, the Shetland pony's main job is to give rides to kids at carnivals and birthday parties. Most of them wish they were back in the coal mines where they at least had their dignity.

Seven slithery, slimy slugs
Sliding through the yard.
Oozing trails of gooey stuff.
For slugs it's not too hard.

Slugs are gastropod mollusks, whatever that means. They have two sets of tentacles: an upper pair for detecting light and a lower pair for smelling. If a tentacle gets lost (now where did I put that tentacle?), the slug can simply grow a new one.

A slug secretes slime so it can slide along on its "foot" without scraping itself raw. Other slugs use these trails of slime as super highways leading to the best and freshest produce for dinner.

The slime is also a defense. Who wants to eat something that leaves a yucky-tasting slime in your mouth all day?

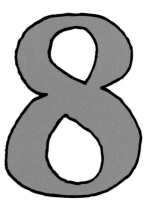

Eight elegant elephants
On a trampoline,
All dressed up in tutus pink
And boas colored green.

Elephants are the largest land animals. They have poor eyesight and, despite their large ears, they have poor hearing. They do, however, have a very good sense of smell.

Elephants sleep just four hours a day and eat for 16—which leaves only four hours for watching TV.

The most prominent feature on an elephant is its trunk, which has 40 thousand muscles in it. Or 100 thousand. Experts aren't sure because they keep losing count around 38½ thousand.

Elephants walk on their tiptoes and, without a trampoline, can't jump. This is one of the reasons why so few of them play basketball.

Nine nervous nanny goats
Waiting for the bus
"Egads! The driver's
    really late!"
They're making quite a fuss.

Goats have been domesticated for 10,000 years, but you wouldn't guess that from watching them eat. They eat like animals! And they eat almost anything.

Goats, like cows, chew cud. And like cows, they give milk which is drunk by humans—by more humans than drink cow's milk. Goats are quite proud of this fact. And worldwide, more goat meat is eaten by humans than cow's meat. Goats are neither proud of nor happy about this fact.

10

Ten charging cheetahs
  spotted
Shopping at the store,
Buying things they can't
  afford
And then they buy
  some more.

Cheetahs are fast animals. Very fast. They can reach speeds up to 75 miles per hour—27 miles per hour in school zones.

The cheetah, however, is a fraidy cat. It will leave its dinner—sometimes its lunch—to just about any menacing animal that wants it. The cheetah's livelihood depends on its speed and it can't afford to get hurt. Plus, cheetahs have notoriously poor health insurance.

Cheetahs can't growl, can't retract their claws all the way and they aren't very good at long division.

11

Eleven balding eagles
In a barber shop,
"Take a bit from off
   the sides
But please don't touch
   the top!"

The bald eagle is America's national bird. Bald eagles mate for life and build the largest nests of any North American birds. These nests can measure up to eight feet wide and 13 feet deep, and can weigh thousands of pounds. A 30-year, fixed-rate mortgage is not uncommon for these nests.

Bald eagles' favorite food is fish and their second favorite food is dead fish—which is why bald eagles usually live near large bodies of water. Or, sushi restaurants.

12

Twelve pugnacious penguins
Playing on the ice—
Hooking, slashing, tripping—
They don't play very nice.

There are 17 different species of penguins. Or 18. Scientists, for being so good at so many things, can sometimes be pretty poor counters.

Emperors, the largest of the penguins, reach heights up to three-and-a-half feet. The smallest penguins, the fairy or little blue penguins, stand a diminutive 16 inches. Prehistoric penguins were as tall as humans. Of course, some prehistoric humans were only as tall as penguins.

No one knows for sure where the name "penguin" came from. It could very easily have come from New Jersey.

13

Thirteen thirsty theropods
Drinking cups of tea;
Sipping with their pinkies up,
Polite as you and me.

Theropods first appeared on Earth
220 million years ago last August.
Tyrannosaurus Rex, probably the best
known of these ferocious beasts, was
recently bumped down the list of biggest
theropods to the number four position.
T-Rex, however, still has the coolest
name: "Oh my, I'm scared to death, here
comes a Spinosaurus aegyptiacus!"

Descendants of the blood-thirsty
theropods that still exist today include
parakeets and sparrows.

14

Fourteen frisky froggies
Playing at the pool;
Laughing, splashing,
  having fun,
Staying very cool.

Frogs are very versatile and adaptable animals. They were hopping around on this earth when those ferocious theropods were still alive.

Frogs absorb water through their skin—which is why you never see them using straws.

A frog's tongue is sticky, folded up and attached to the front of its mouth. This greatly helps the frog catch and eat small insects but isn't too handy when it comes to eating spaghetti.

15

Fifteen crazy crawdads
Going round and round.
Some are riding horses,
Some are riding hounds.

Crawdads are small cousins—
about one-third the size—of lobsters.
What they lack for in size, they more
than make up for in names. Lobsters
are called lobsters. Crawdads are
called crayfish, crawfish, spoondogs,
muddogs and yabbies. And who
knows what other names they've got
in China, France and Spain?

Crawdads eat snails, algae, insect
larvae, worms, and tadpoles. They are
not very partial to Cajun cooking.

16

Sixteen platypuses
(Duck-billed ones, of course)
Parachuting from a plane,
They screamed so loud
they're hoarse.

The platypus is a mammal, but just barely. It has legs on its sides like a lizard. It's venomous, like a snake. It lays eggs like a chicken. And, it has a duckbill… like a duck.

Its bill isn't just for good looks. It uses it to dig through mud, searching for food. Its bill also has high-tech receptors that sense electrical fields generated by the muscles of its prey. If you're being stalked by a platypus, be still, be very still: don't move a muscle.

17

Seventeen silly swordfish
Swimming in the sea,
Maybe just a bit too close,
Wounding accidentally.

   Swordfish don't have any teeth, at least adult swordfish don't. And if that's not bad enough, adult swordfish don't have any scales either.

   What they do have are impressive snouts which they use for thrashing through schools of fish, stunning or killing their prey. Then they turn quickly for a bite or two to eat.

   Their favorite foods? Tuna fish (fresh, never canned), barracuda, mackerel, squid, and flying fish (business class only).

18

Eighteen loafing lizards
Working in a shop,
Baking lots of loaves of bread
Crisscrossed on the top.

Most lizards have four legs with five toes on each foot. But some lizards have no legs and no toes on the feet they don't have.

Most lizards have an acute sense of smell, but they don't use their noses for smelling. (Then how do they smell? Awful.) They flick out their tongues, grab some scents and bring them back into their mouths where a vomeronasal organ (a fancy term for "a sort of nose-like thing in the mouth") processes the odors.

There are LOTS of different kinds of lizards. And one of the weirdest, the horned lizard, can squirt blood from its eyes! They do it mainly to confuse and scare predators, but it's also a pretty cool party trick.

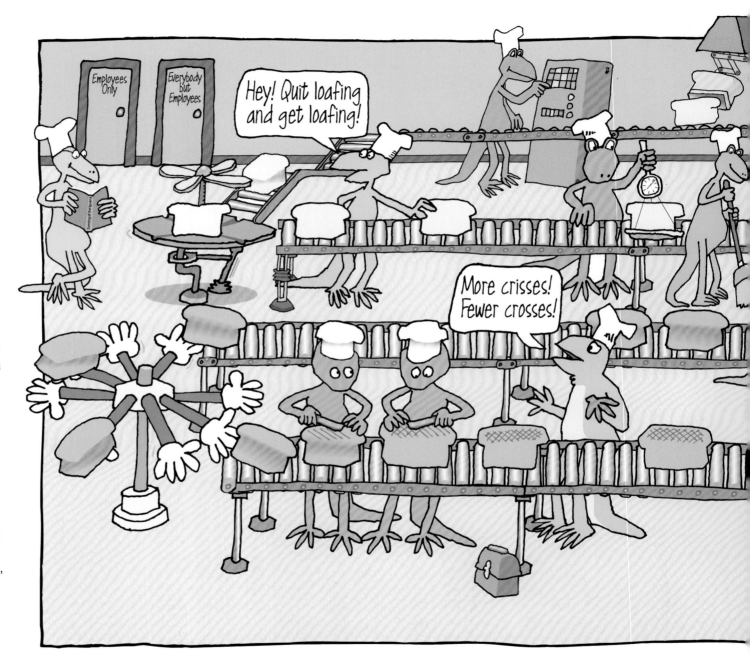

19

Nineteen weary woodchucks,
Working without rest,
Chuck, chuck, chucking
   chopped up wood
It's what they do the best.

   Woodchucks didn't get their name because they like tossing around pieces of lumber. Their Cree Indian name was "wuchak," which early colonists mispronounced. Woodchucks are also called groundhogs, marmots, lawn beavers and whistle pigs.

   Woodchucks may not be good at chucking wood, but they are good diggers. In excavating a burrow, a woodchuck can move up to 700 pounds of dirt, creating nearly 45 feet of tunnels.

   They eat all summer long and after the first frost, they hibernate—until they have to get up, on February 2, to let everyone know whether winter is over or will last another six weeks.

20

Twenty monkeys reading
  books
At the library.
What is it that they're
  reading?
Look closely and you'll see.

Monkeys live in complex societies, communicate with gestures, use tools and even like to gamble. What truly separates them from humans is that they don't run up huge credit-card bills.

There are Old World monkeys and New World monkeys. The largest of the New World monkeys are the howler monkeys, who are also the loudest animals in North America. Their howls can easily be heard through three miles of thick jungle. You don't want to be sitting in front of a couple of howler monkeys when you're watching a movie in a theater!